D0251450

Dominique de Saint Mars

Après des études de sociologie,
elle a été journaliste à *Astrapi*.
Elle écrit des histoires
qui donnent la parole aux enfants
et traduisent leurs émotions.
Elle dit en souriant qu'elle a interviewé
au moins 100 000 enfants...
Ses deux fils, Arthur et Henri,
ont été ses premiers inspirateurs !
Prix de la Fondation pour l'Enfance.
Auteur de *On va avoir un bébé*,
Je grandis, *Les Filles et les Garçons*,
Passeport pour l'école,
et *Léon a deux maisons*.

Serge Bloch

Cet observateur plein d'humour
et de tendresse est aussi un maître
de la mise en scène.
Tout en distillant son humour généreux
à longueur de cases, il aime faire sentir
la profondeur des sentiments.

Max va à l'hôpital

IMPRIMÉ EN FRANCE

Avec la collaboration de l'équipe de chirurgie
du Professeur Carlioz de l'hôpital Trousseau

© Calligram 1993
© Calligram 1995 pour la présente édition
Tous droits réservés pour tous pays
Imprimé en CEE
ISBN : 2-88445-106-4

Ainsi va la vie

Max va à l'hôpital

Dominique de Saint Mars

Serge Bloch

CALLIGRAM

CHRISTIAN GALLIMARD

9

11

12

15

21

23

24

25

26

27

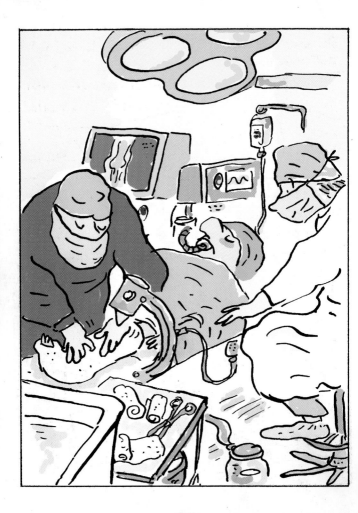

30

LE SOIR...

J'aime pas la nuit, ici, j'ai peur des cauchemars. Je veux voir maman.

Tu la verras demain.

Non, elle ne vient pas demain, on habite loin d'ici.

32

33

40

Et toi...

Est-ce qu'il t'est arrivé la même histoire qu'à Max ?

ça a fait mal !.. mais je me vengerai...

As-tu eu mal ? As-tu eu peur, en as-tu parlé ?

au secours !..

Quel a été ton plus mauvais souvenir ?

Quel a été ton meilleur souvenir ?

Est-ce que tu as demandé que l'on t'explique
ce que tu ne comprenais pas ?

Est-ce que tu t'es fait des copains ou des copines ?

As-tu rencontré des enfants qui avaient
des problèmes plus graves que toi ?

Es-tu allé voir des gens qui y étaient ?

As-tu des amis qui y sont allés ?

Comment l'imagines-tu ?

De quoi aurais-tu peur ?

Aimerais-tu, plus tard, avoir un métier
pour soigner les gens ?

Penses-tu qu'un séjour à l'hôpital ou à la clinique
peut avoir des bons côtés ?

**Après avoir réfléchi
à ces questions
sur l'hôpital et la clinique,
tu peux en parler
avec tes parents ou tes amis.**

was whether it made itself vulnerable to a serious breach each time it brought on a consultant or new employee. "Most systems are like a Tootsie Pop," Seiden said. "They have this hard, crunchy outside but they're very gooey and soft on the inside. Once you get past that crunchy outside and you're inside, you can do anything."

The first thing Seiden did was log on to a computer and probe the bank's digital defenses. Invariably, that was step one. He used scanning tools to reveal any obvious vulnerabilities: whether the organization was using a default password or a weak one, or whether its IT people had failed to install a known patch. When those didn't reveal any security holes, he resorted to plan B, or what he called "the physical thing." He would try to obtain the bank's secrets in the physical world rather than over a computer network.

Seiden began showing his face at the bank during the day to get people used to seeing him while also scoping things out. Mainly, though, he worked at night, when there weren't prying eyes watching what he was doing. Perusing an employee directory, he figured out where the head of facilities worked. "This guy has a title like associate vice president but no private office," Seiden said. He located the

man's work area, where he found a locked cabinet. Using a paperclip, Seiden broke into it. Inside, he found floor plans and keys to its facilities around the world. He copied the floor plans before putting them back. The keys he took.

Another find during one of these nocturnal scavenger hunts was the bank's backup tapes, boxed and ready f pickup. This was pre–"cloud computing," when busine backed up their computer files on thick magnetic generally stored at another location. "So I walke with a set of backups," he said. Later, he was sho the information on the tapes had not been "You'd think a company like that would knov its backup tapes," he said, shaking his head. tape reader picked up at any Office Depo could mine the confidential customer data tapes.

On another night, Seiden visited employee in charge of the bank's pho lots of secrets on voice mails," he be really cool to get voice-mail with those in hand, he could the CEO and those occupyi bank's top lawyer, say, or

This seemed Seiden's favorite part of the story. Sitting at a restaurant in San Francisco's Mission District, a mischievous grin appeared on his face. He adjusted his glasses and pursed his lips to suppress a smile as he told me about returning to the same conference room where he had first taken the assignment barely a month earlier. His contact and another man appeared shocked, he said, as he revealed what he learned, including the names of their clients and the dollar amounts they had paid.

Seiden returned the keys and tapes he had taken, along with any copies he had made. He pointed out how easily he had obtained the passwords that would let him eavesdrop on voice mails, and other vulnerabilities he had uncovered. He also asked them what, if anything, they had heard about the things he had taken. No one had reported that the backup tapes had gone missing but that was easy enough to explain: presumably, people assumed they had been picked up, as happened every month. But no one had reported the missing keys. When they confronted the facilities manager, he confessed to replacing them with a set copied from a colleague. Because of Seiden's assignment, the head of facilities would be granted an office, though it's a safe bet that it would not be occupied by the same person holding the job during Seiden's short stint as a bank contractor.

A LOT OF PEN testers stick to the machine. They test a network's outer digital walls, they look for ways to fool a network into allowing them access to places they shouldn't be permitted to go—anything that doesn't require human interaction. Seiden, by contrast, shared exploits that require social skills rather than technical prowess. "Mark is known industry-wide for his more creative solutions to security problems," said Bruce Schneier, a longtime security expert and a lecturer at the Harvard Kennedy School.

Seiden's closet is often his starting point for a job. There he can choose from any number of disguises he has found over the years browsing eBay and rummaging through the racks at thrift shops: a brown UPS uniform, a black-and-purple FedEx polo, a variety of shirts stamped with the names of phone companies or photocopy repair services. Other jobs call for a hard hat (white, like a supervisor would wear) and a clipboard. "You look at the ceiling and act like you know what you're doing and people will generally ignore you," he said. The real challenge is getting inside a facility.

Then, snack and lunch trucks help. "I'll drink coffee near a crew during a break or hang out by the taco truck and walk in with them when it's time for them to go back to work," Seiden said.

"If I get caught, I have this 'get out of jail free' card," he said. "But what's scary is how rarely I have to use it. It's pretty rare that I'm ever confronted by anyone."

Seiden was never the typical hacker. Born and raised in New York City, he was a music prodigy who started playing the piano when he was five. He skipped third grade and then finished middle school in two years instead of three. He attended the prestigious Bronx High School of Science in the 1960s. While there, he spent much of his free time at a research center on NYU's campus that had an early supercomputer but no way for multiple people to interact with the machine simultaneously. Seiden, who had taught himself to program while at Bronx Science, joined a group of students who worked on a program that fixed the problem. MIT offered Seiden a full scholarship but he chose Columbia, he said, "because I didn't want to turn into an engineering nerd."

Seiden was sixteen when he started Columbia, where he majored in math (the school did not yet have a computer science department) but also music and linguistics. It was while working for his college radio station, in 1968, during his sophomore year, that he revealed hints of the gifts that would serve him well once he turned his attention to penetration testing. Student protesters had taken over an administrative building, and then battled the police over the occupation of others. "I taught myself how to make keys to the tunnels under campus," Seiden said, "which let us get from building to building without getting teargassed or beaten up by the cops." Seiden and a reporter from the station would pop up inside a building and then broadcast from there in relative comfort after connecting the station's gear to a campus phone.

Seiden's first job after graduation was as a programmer at a large time-sharing company—except he spent his summers working as a recording engineer, first in Aspen, then in Marlboro, Vermont, both of which host a classical music festival from mid-July to mid-August. That ended when he secured a position with IBM. "IBM Research was too much fun to leave for a summer recording music," he said. While at IBM he returned to Columbia, where he earned a master's in electrical engineering. He moved to the West Coast to join a computer-aided design (CAD) startup that included Lucasfilm (best known for the Star Wars and Indiana Jones franchises) as a client. The startup failed but led to a good-paying consulting gig with Lucasfilm, where he helped the studio make the transition to digital moviemaking. Seiden took on a number of clients over the next decade, including IBM and Morgan Stanley. He described himself as part of the "brain trust" that helped give rise to *Wired*—to the point where his computer served as the company's first e-mail server. He registered the magazine's domain name and occasionally wrote for the print publication.

Seiden's transition from programmer to IT security nerd seemed almost random. A former IBM colleague working at First Data, a credit card processor, enlisted Seiden to help them solve a cutting-edge problem in the early 1990s: securely using a credit card to make an online payment. "First Data decided they would set up a way to take credit cards over the internet," Seiden said. "And I was hired to do their firewalls." He was new to security but he saw how the previous twenty years had been the ideal training ground to think about setting up digital defenses. "If you don't know how to create a program, it's going to be that much harder to figure out how to break into one."

His work as a pen tester started gradually. The work required him to sign an NDA—a non-disclosure agreement—so Seiden wasn't able to name the companies that hired him. But a friend recommended him for his first pen-testing job and then one assignment led to another. Sometimes they were solo gigs; other times he was asked to join a "red team," which is when a company hires a small group of outsiders to test its defenses. He had other clients, including Xerox PARC, but the work that most interested him then were design reviews and vulnerability testing. By the mid-2000s, pen testing accounted for roughly 80 percent of his work.

Eventually, Seiden's pen testing led to a full-time job with Yahoo and its fabled security team, known internally as the "Paranoids." Yahoo had started as a client—one of any number of companies that had hired him as a pen tester. "We'd bring in all these remote Paranoids, consultants, and speakers from around the world to the main office in Sunnyvale, California, for 'paranoid week,'" said George Neville-Neil, who had gone to work at Yahoo a couple of years before Seiden joined the company. "I remember being really impressed with a talk on physical security that Mark gave." Seiden did pen testing after joining Yahoo full-time but also served as one of the company's top firefighters working incident response.

Like most internet companies, Yahoo rented space at what are called co-location centers, or "colos"—data centers around the globe that house servers for multiple businesses in giant, many-storied buildings outfitted with generators, air-cooling equipment, and presumably the requisite security. The deals often included the right to test a facility's vulnerabilities, a job that often fell to Seiden and George Neville-Neil.

On one trip, the pair visited a particularly tall data center in Hong Kong. The two theorized that if they could gain access to other parts of the building, anyone renting space there could gain access to theirs. On the elevator, "Mark picks this cheap lock and pulls down the panel cover," Neville-Neil said. "Meanwhile, I'm making sure my bald head is reflecting light into the cameras so people can't see us. He then throws this switch and we're able to go to any floor we wanted." Once off the elevator, getting into another company's colo area proved easy. They noticed that the wires for a magnetic lock ran on the outside of a heavy, metal fire door. They interrupted the electrical circuit and the door just popped open. On another floor, they found that the wires for an electronic reader a company had installed were exposed. Again, getting inside proved as simple as touching two wires together and short-circuiting the device.

Seiden was more brazen than Neville-Neil—to the point where Neville-Neil was frightened when the two were scheduled to travel to mainland China. Neville-Neil had seen Seiden swipe the "passbook" that security guards use to write out passes when letting people into a data center. "A security guard leaves the book unattended and now you can come in with a pass any time you want," Neville-Neil said. Unlike him, Seiden would attempt to pick a lock even when he knew there was a camera pointed at it. "One time," Neville-Neal continued, "he's someplace he shouldn't be and he's holding a sign that reads HELP. No one even noticed." He loved his partner's flamboyant ways but begged Seiden to avoid any of his more outlandish stunts in Beijing. "I told him, 'Fucking get me arrested in Beijing and I will shiv you in the shower.'"

SEIDEN LEFT YAHOO AT the beginning of 2012, a year before the company suffered two of the Web's worst-